Jaw-dropping adventure comics from

SWORDS, SHIPS & SUPLEXES!

sweatdrop
droplets

Hello there! I'm guessing you're the type of person that:
A) Loves comic books and manga
B) Has a wild imagination and dreams of going on adventures
C) Likes sword fighting, sailing ships and/or wrestling suplexes
D) Is totally awesome
E) ALL OF THE ABOVE

If that's the case, WELCOME! This book was made just for you.
We've taken our best adventure ideas, mixed in a dollop of
excitement, a pinch of peril and a lot of fun, and spread them all
out in this book ready for reading. It's up to you whether you
pick a page to jump into, or read through from the beginning -
each story is a new adventure.

We really hope you'll enjoy reading this book! And if you do,
don't be selfish - why not share it with your grown-ups? They
might enjoy it too. After all, they were just like you when they
were younger. And everyone should have fun reading comics,
no matter how old they are.

Much love,
Sonia!

Cover Art by Rebecca Burgess
Graphic design by En Gingerboom

Published by Sweatdrop Studios.
www.sweatdrop.com

ISBN 978-1905038664

Printed in UK
First printing November 2022

CONTENTS

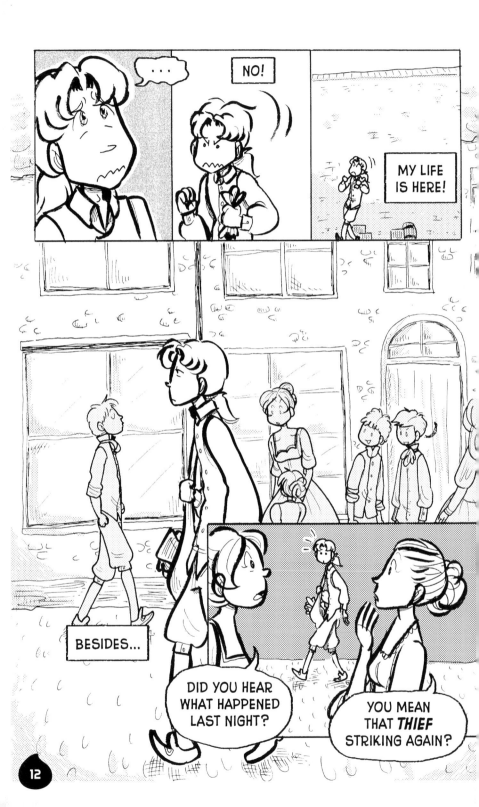

UNFORTUNATELY,

WHILE I'VE BEEN WANDERING THE NIGHT HELPING PEOPLE AND DOING GOOD DEEDS...

SOMEONE ELSE HAS BEEN LURKING AROUND DOING **BAD DEEDS.** AN EVIL BANDIT!

GREETINGS, CITIZENS!

?!!

AND MY FIRST GOOD DEED TONIGHT IS...

MEW!

RESCUING A CAT.

WELL, IN A TOWN LIKE THIS...

MY ADVENTURES ARE KIND OF SMALL, I GUESS.

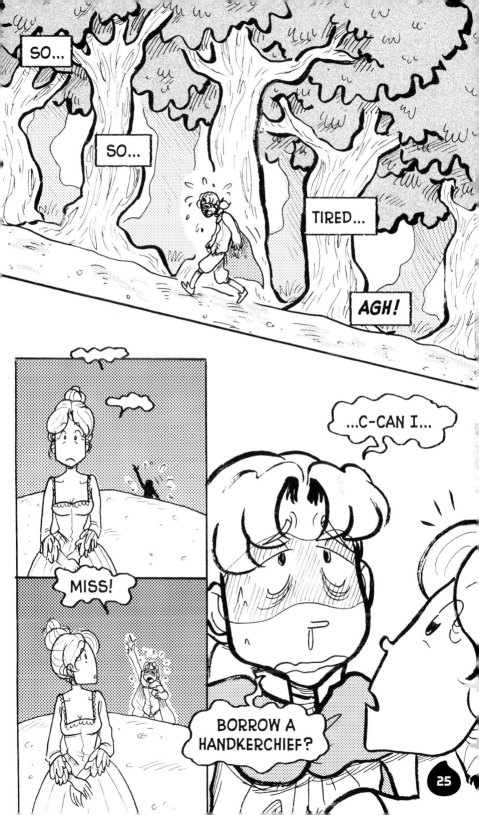

AND IT ONLY HAS ROOM FOR ONE PERSON.

THE PERSON I'M **MEANT** TO BE.

AND BECOME...

IT'S TIME TO GIVE UP THE BROADSHEET SELLER!

YAAAAAYYY!!!

HE'S LEAVING!

WOO! YES!

...CHEERING?

THAT'S ODD.

WAIT.

I KNEW IT.

A DIFFERENT KIND OF ADVENTURE

MORAG LEWIS

BEING A PIRATE'S AMAZING!

WE GET ALL THE BEST ADVENTURES!

ADVENTURES DON'T SCARE ME.

I ATE THE TEN-TENTACLED SQUID-BEAST AFTER IT ATTACKED THE SHIP.

OLD MO COOKED IT UP.

IT TASTED LIKE OLD ROPE BOILED IN VINEGAR.

SNF!

50

A DIFFERENT KIND OF ADVENTURE, HUH?

THE END

68

JUST SIT DOWN AND LET THE TEAPOT POUR YOU SOME TEA.

OH, AND DON'T FORGET THE SUGAR!

IMAGINE HOW MUCH TIME THE WORLD WILL SAVE IF BREAKFAST CAN MAKE ITSELF!

Yes!

UHM...

mew!

YOU FORGOT THE HONEY THOUGH.

WHAT?

NO WAY!

I MADE THE HONEY FIRST, 'COS IT'S YOUR FAVOURITE.

THERE'S JAM, MUSTARD, MARMALADE, BUTTER, MILK...

NO HONEY.

HUH...

DO ANY OF YOU GUYS...

...HAPPEN TO KNOW ANYTHING ABOUT THIS?

WELL?

eek!

Wah!

YOU'LL NEVER MEET ANY BEES WAY UP HERE.

KNOW IT ALL

I KNOW!

THEY'RE ALL DOWN THERE.

PREPARE FOR LANDING.

Putt

Putt Putt

AAAH, FIRM GROUND...

SUCH A RELIEF!

THIS IS NO TIME TO LAZE AROUND!

UH...

NOW WHAT WOULD BE THE BEST WAY TO INTRODUCE MYSELF TO THE BEES... I KNOW, I'LL KNOCK!

I DON'T THINK THAT'S SUCH A GOOD IDEA!

OH, WHAT'S THE WORST THAT COULD HAPPEN?

KNOCK KNOCK

WOW, THAT'S A *LOT* OF BEES!

OH HONOURED BEES, I HAVE A QUESTION I NEED YOUR HELP WITH.

HAVE YOU SEEN A JAR OF HONEY?

ABOUT SO BIG?

OH, THANK-YOU!

RIGHT, TEAM, LET'S GO!

fwip fwip

E-EVERYONE?

Rustle

WHAT ARE YOU TWO DOING HIDING? WE'RE GOING.

mew

I'M *SCARED OF* BEES, YOU KNOW.

OH NONSENSE. THESE GUYS ARE FRIENDLY...

...SEE!

beemoji

bzz

bzz

whew

I THINK I PREFERRED THE TERRIFYING FLYING VACUUM.

OH SHUSH, WE'RE ALMOST THERE...

WHILE WE WAIT, DID YOU KNOW IT'S A MYTH THAT A BUMBLE BEE'S FLIGHT DEFIES PHYSICS?
IT'S BASED ON A MISTAKEN IDEA THAT THEIR WINGS JUST MOVE UP AND DOWN. INSTEAD THEY ROTATE A LITTLE TOO, MAKING TINY VORTEXES TO GIVE THEM LIFT! IT'S REALLY CLEVER!

81

REAL BRAVERY IS LETTING YOUR FRIENDS HELP YOU. REAL BRAVERY IS TRUSTING ME AND COMING HOME.

SORRY, JAM, I CAN'T COME BACK UNTIL I'VE PROVED MYSELF.

GOODBYE...

NOOO!!

HMM...

KITTY, COME HERE! QUICK!

- —— LATER —— -

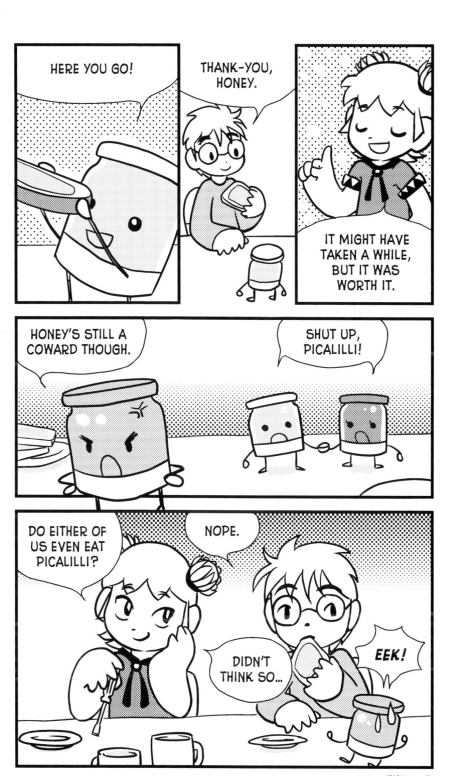

THE END

All For Fun

by Sonia Leong

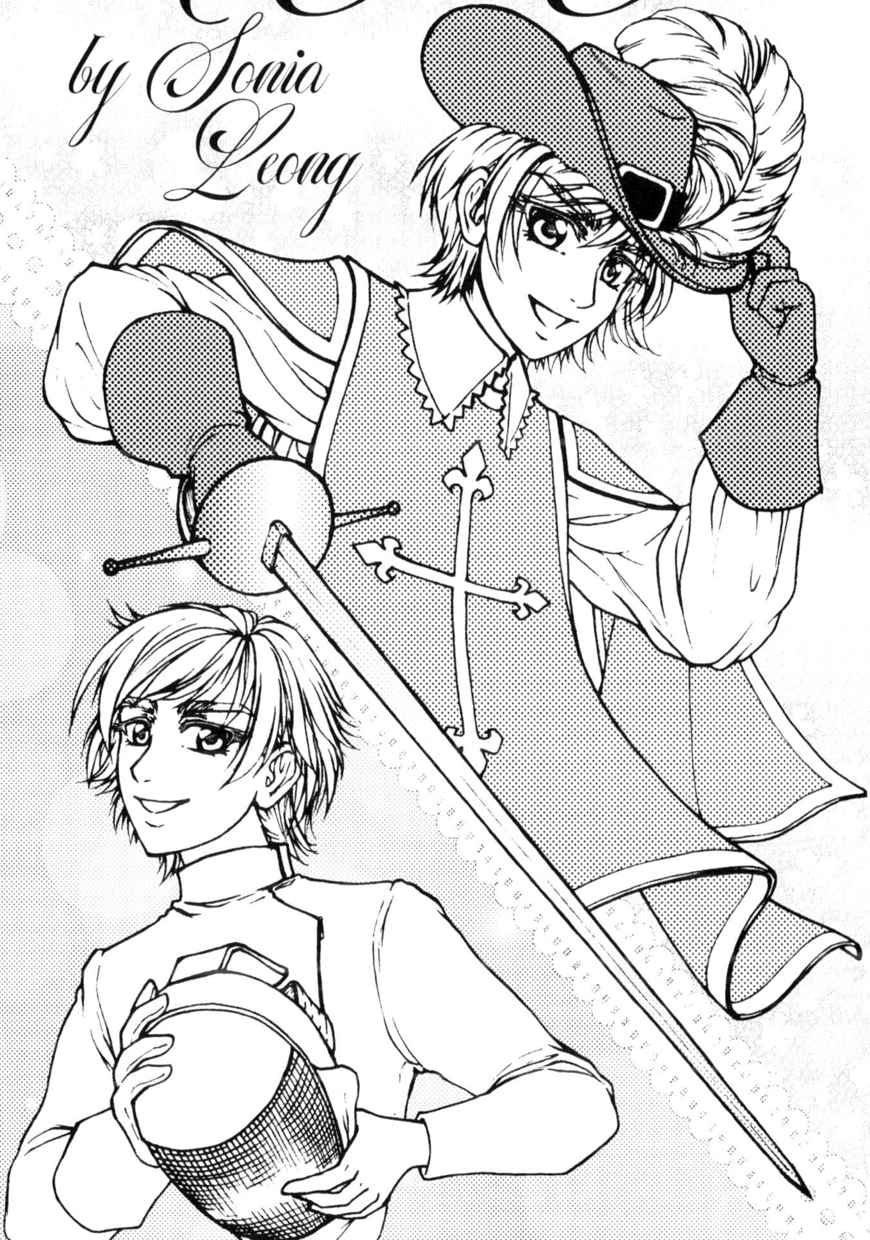

THE FINAL ROUNDS OF THE NATIONAL YOUTH FENCING CHAMPIONSHIPS WILL BEGIN SHORTLY—

STARTING WITH THE BOY'S UNDER 12 FOIL.

CLAP

CLAP

CLAP

HEY, IS THAT THE FINALIST?

YEAH, KIERAN KNIGHT. HE'S LIKE, THE BEST IN THE COUNTRY-

I'VE SEEN HIM ON TV!

OMIGOSH, NO WAY! HE'S SOOOO CUTE TOO!

HE'S ON NEXT, I CAN'T WAIT TO SEE HIM FENCE! HE'LL WIN FOR SURE!

...sigh...

ALLEZ!

FWIP

THNK!

TOUCHÉ! CLEAN ONE.

WHEN EVERYONE EXPECTS SO MUCH...

YOU'RE GOING THROUGH ALL THE MOTIONS

JUST TO GET IT OVER AND DONE WITH.

...

SO!

WHY D'YOU GET INTO FENCING ANYWAY?

THEN IT'S SETTLED!

YOU... ARE D'ARTAGNAN!

AND HE...

IS ONE OF CARDINAL RICHELIEU'S MEN!

BUT THAT'S JUST BEING SILLY!

107

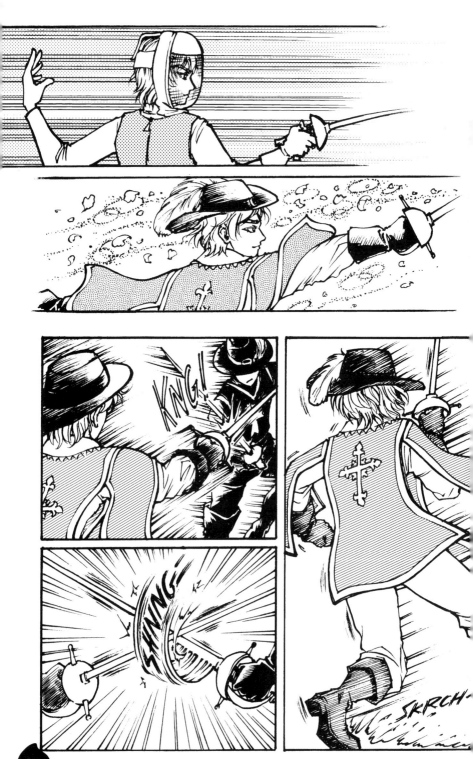

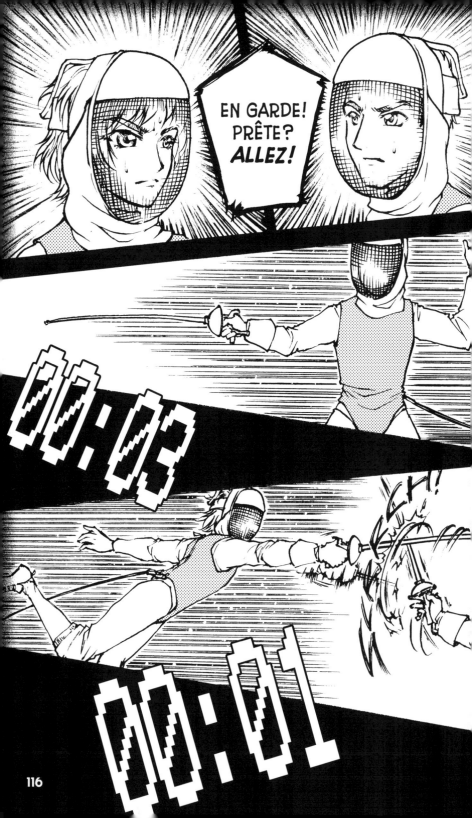

The End.

123

CAT'S CRADLE SUPLEX!

HAND THAT BELT OVER, LIONESSA!

YOU'LL CATCH UP! I'M ONLY A YEAR OLDER!

FINE! I'LL NEVER BE AS GOOD AS YOU, MEL!

PLUS THAT'S WHAT TAG-TEAMS ARE FOR!

GOTTA WORK TOGETHER!

ONE WEEK LATER

I'VE COME TO SAY BYE ...

IT TAKES 5 HOURS TO GET TO THE NEW HOUSE! UGH!

I'LL WRITE YOU WHEN WE GET THERE!

I'M GOING TO MISS YOU SO MUCH, HAN!

ME TOO, MEL. WE'LL ALWAYS BE FRIENDS!

129

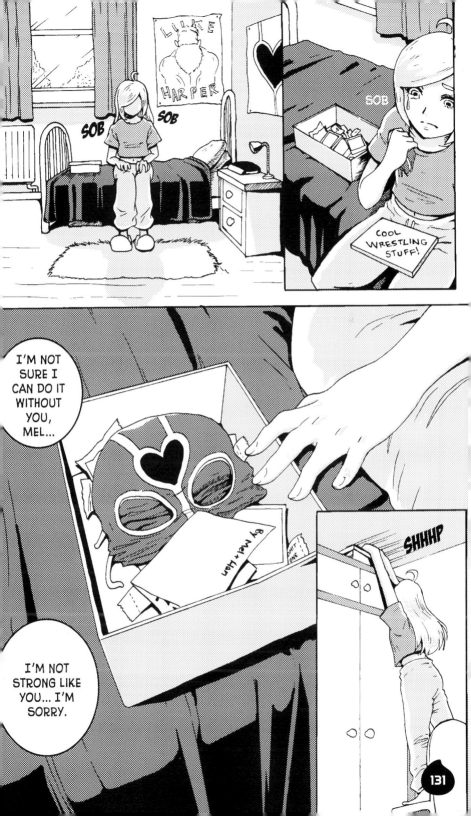

AND SCARLET HAS HER LOCKED IN HER GRIP!

HNNGH...

CHOP!

OH, THOSE STRIKES ARE BRUTAL!

SQUEEZE

THAT'S IT! THE CATS CRADLE SUPLEX!

146

147

SORRY ABOUT THIS.

ORDERS FROM THE HOUSE.

I BOUGHT A TICKET! I PROMISE!

BACKSTAGE →

DRESSING ROOM

?

THERE.

151

THWIP

YOU WERE SO GOOD!

WELL, I HAVE BEEN PRACTISING FOR, LIKE, TWO YEARS!

GOT A TAG TEAM DREAM TO FULFILL, RIGHT?

154

YAAAAAY!

u no wot, ur right. i'm @ wrestling. rather b here than joe's, u shuldn't b there urself n u no it. Sik of bein ur excuse wen u mess things up.

BEEP

BEEP

157

NOTHING CAN STOP US AND OUR AMAZING MAGICAL DROPLET POWERS!
TOGETHER WE'LL EMBARK ON THIS DANGEROUS MISSION, AND-
SUE!
CAN YOU PLEASE GO TO THE POST OFFICE ALREADY?
PICK UP MILK WHILE YOU'RE THERE TOO.
AH, YOUR MUM SOUNDS ANNOYED
HOW'S THIS FOR AN ADVENTURE, SUETO?
WELL, YOU KNOW WHAT THEY SAY, SHUGA!
LIFE IS WHAT YOU MAKE IT!
THE END

FOR GROWN-UPS

Thanks so much for reading our book!
Sweatdrop Studios is a UK-based independent publisher and comic collaborative, and Sweatdrop Droplets is our imprint for younger readers.

If you'd like to read more of our works suitable for younger audiences, have a look at the next few pages to see what takes your fancy, then head to our website to directly order from us at www.sweatdrop.com

The members of Sweatdrop Studios have worked with many schools, libraries, museums and bookstores to deliver comic/Manga workshops for all ages. If you would like to organise something, please email us at workshop@sweatdrop.com

Would you like to commission one of our comic artists to draw your friends/family as a unique gift?
Email commissions@sweatdrop.com

STAFF

SONIA LEONG
DIRECTOR - EDITOR

EN GINGERBOOM
DESIGNER - EDITOR

The Masked Thief
REBECCA BURGESS - REBECCABURGESS.CO.UK

FAVOURITE KIND OF ADVENTURE?
A cosy one that looks like a country-side walk, with apple pie at the end.

A Different Kind of Adventure
MORAG LEWIS - TOOTHYCAT.NET

FAVOURITE KIND OF ADVENTURE?
I like journeys, exploring new worlds and hearing new stories.

Honey Be Brave
SELINA DEAN - NODDINGCAT.NET

FAVOURITE KIND OF ADVENTURE?
Stories set in the real world; to see the hidden corners other people find.

All For Fun
SONIA LEONG - FYREDRAKE.NET

FAVOURITE KIND OF ADVENTURE?
Stuff with cool weapons and epic battles! Because I'm all about the action!

Cat-Astrophe!
RUTH KEATTCH - RUTHKEATTCH.CO.UK

FAVOURITE KIND OF ADVENTURE?
Chasing your dreams, bringing hope and light, and having amazing fun!

Magical Girl Sueto
EN GINGERBOOM - ENGINGERBOOM.CO.UK

FAVOURITE KIND OF ADVENTURE?
A space-faring journey; I want to meet alien life and see alien worlds!

VARIOUS AUTHORS

Sweatdrop Studios presents you with a collection of tales adapted from stories well-loved and time-tested. Contained within these pages you'll find fables from near and far; some will shock, some will surprise and some will make you smile. Sweatdrop's artists have scoured the globe for stories that have inspired and touched them in some way, and we hope that they'll do the same for you.

ISBN: 9781905038282

Fantasy, Adventure

JOANNA ZHOU

A super-kawaii childhood adventure!

After getting lost in a supermarket, little Ken meets an unexpected companion on the cookie shelf. Together they embark on an important, and quite tasty, quest. Includes a bonus section of 4-koma strips and artist comments.

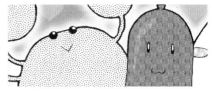

Comedy, Drama

CREATING

CREATING
MANGA CHARACTERS

VARIOUS AUTHORS

Characters are an essential component of manga. They are also enormous fun to imagine and to draw, but it's not always easy to fit your characters, your world and your plot together.

This book describes the process of character creation and how your character could express their personality and emotions. Five original characters help to explain every topic, including character traits, from personalities and typical roles all the way down to the individual details important to make your character unique. Packed with tips, it describes how to make your world realistic and intriguing.

Published by Crowood Press.

ISBN: 978184797381 *Instruction*

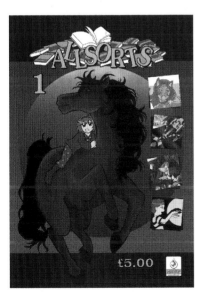

MORAG LEWIS, EMMA VIECELI, EN GINGERBOOM

Legend says there's a kelpie in the loch by Molly's house. Molly doesn't really believe it's true, but something draws her to the loch shore at night. Something she longs for, something that will be hers alone, not her twin sister's. Something like riding a water horse...

A collection of short stories, four comics and one text with pictures, for readers of 8 and up.

Fantasy, Sci-Fi

CATALOGUE

ANTHOLOGIES & MAGAZINES

Blue is for Boys	Various Authors
Cold Sweat and Tears	Various Authors
Drop Dead Monstrous	Various Authors
Pink is for Girls	Various Authors
Shimmering Drop	Various Authors
Sparkling Drop	Various Authors
Stardust	Various Authors
Sugardrops	Various Authors
Swords, Ships & Suplexes	Various Authors
Telling Tales	Various Authors
The Drop	Various Authors

GRAPHIC NOVELS & BOOKS

A Pocketful of Clouds	Morag Lewis
Ambient Rhythm	Morag Lewis
Aya Takeo	Sonia Leong
Chemical Blue	Irina Richards
Dragon Heir: Reborn	Emma Vieceli
Fantasma	Selina Dean
Jarred	Ruth Keattch
Looking for the Sun	Morag Lewis
Love Stuffing	Sonia Leong
Nobody's Library	Morag Lewis
Once Upon a Time...	Sonia Leong
Patchwork Sky	Morag Lewis
Pearls and Twine	Selina Dean
Sun Fish Moon Fish	Morag Lewis
Sushi and the Beginning of the World	Selina Dean
The Chronicles of Ciel	Sonia Leong
The Witch-Hare	Irina Richards
Trade Winds	Morag Lewis
White Violet	Shazleen Khan

COMICS & SINGLE ISSUES

Allsorts	Morag Lewis, Emma Vieceli and En Gingerboom
All That Matters	Morag Lewis
Artifaxis	Morag Lewis
Bell Ringers	Selina Dean
Chocoberry	Joanna Zhou
Defenders of the Sunset City	Morag Lewis
FujoFujo	Sonia Leong
Harajuku Zoo	Joanna Zhou
Jigsaw Pieces	Morag Lewis
Koneko	Selina Dean
Letters to England	Rebecca Burgess
Mini Murder Mysteries	Morag Lewis
Rel El	En Gingerboom
Sunny's Field	Selina Dean
Sushi and the End of the World	Selina Dean
The Triad	Rowan Clair
Twenty Thirty Three	En Gingerboom
Views From Another Place	Sergei and Morag Lewis

sweatdrop studios
INDEPENDENT ART & COMICS COLLABORATIVE